*For Mum & Dad, from your*
*loving daughter Colleen Waring ~ C M*

**LITTLE TIGER PRESS**
An imprint of Magi Publications
1 The Coda Centre, 189 Munster Road, London SW6 6AW
www.littletigerpress.com

First published in Great Britain 2008

Text and illustrations copyright © Colleen McKeown 2008
Colleen McKeown has asserted her right
to be identified as the author and illustrator of this work under the
Copyright, Designs and Patents Act, 1988

A CIP catalogue record for this book is available from the British Library

Printed in Singapore

2 4 6 8 10 9 7 5 3 1

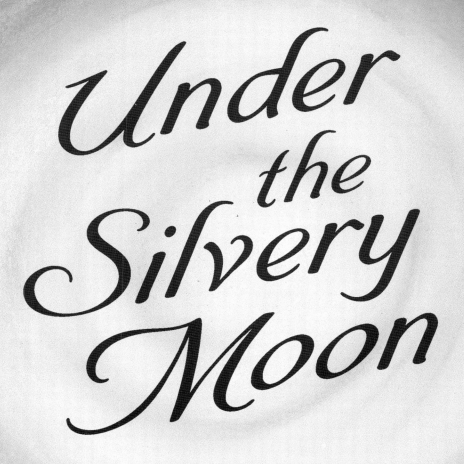

# Under the Silvery Moon

Colleen McKeown

**LITTLE TIGER PRESS**

London

The stars were shining brightly.
Little kitten was in bed.
But up he sat, still wide awake,
"Sleep now," his mother said.

"But it's so noisy, I can't sleep!"
said kitten, with a cry.
"It's just our friends," said mother cat.
"They're waking up nearby . . .

The tiny mice are playing;
    they explore the barn at night.
They skip and scamper here and there,
    beneath the warm lamplight.

Hush, kitten, can you hear it,
that shuffling, snuffling sound?
The hedgehogs look for food to eat
along the moonlit ground.

That cry you hear, so long and loud,
that distant, haunting tune,
belongs to fox who's up at night.
He's calling to the moon.

Around us swirls a summer song;
    it's whispered through the trees.
The evening wind is blowing
    through the softly rustling leaves.

Beyond the midnight meadow,
     where the air is soft and cool,
The frogs are gently croaking
     all around the moonlit pool.

Some creatures are not stirring;
they do not make a peep.
Like us they've had a busy day,
and now they're fast asleep.

The badgers stretch their sturdy legs,
and blink into the dark.
'Good evening,' they are calling,
with a deep and playful bark.

The nimble hares are dancing;
      their paws thump on the ground.
With joyful leaps they chase their tails
      and spring and dart around.

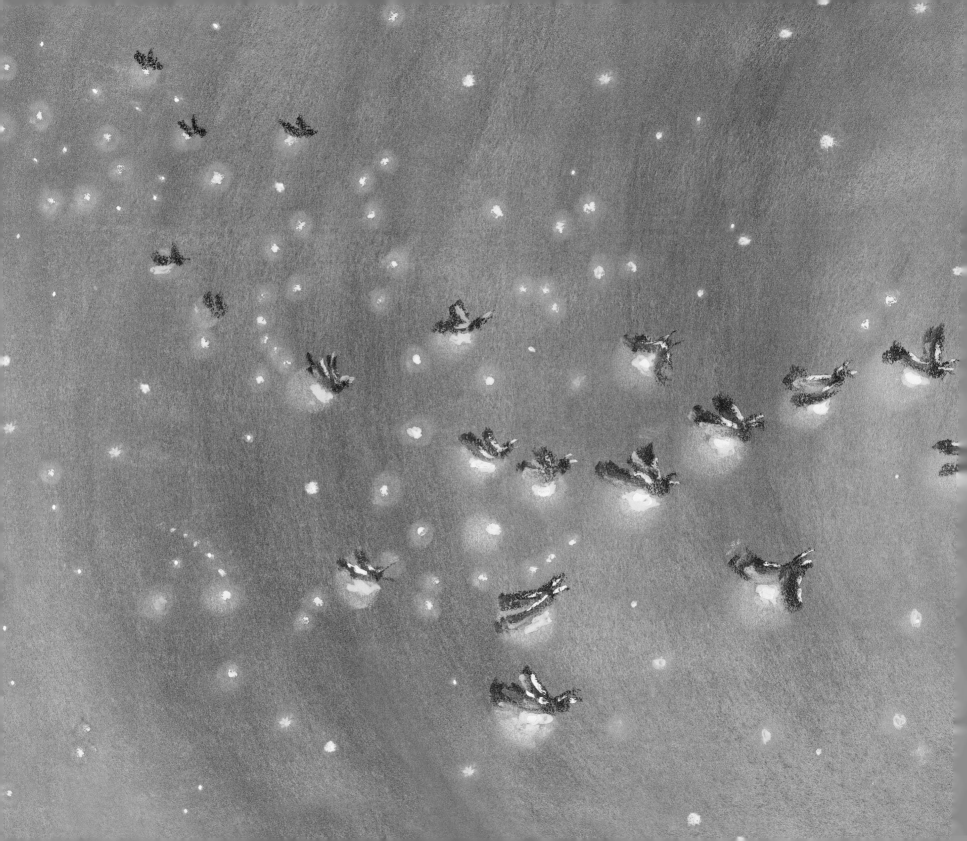

Something quiet and gentle
      lights up the dark, night skies.
Glowing warm and lovely
      are the dreamy fireflies.

Owl is hooting softly;
across the stars she glides.
Soaring home towards the barn,
upon the wind she rides.

And so you see, my little one,
    there's nothing you should fear.
Our friends' night-time adventures
    are all that you can hear."

Little kitten closed his eyes
    and hugged his mother tight.
"It's time you went to sleep," she purred.
    "Sweet dreams, my love, goodnight."